ORIGO
STEPPING STONES

CORE MATHEMATICS

SENIOR AUTHORS

Rosemary Irons
James Burnett

PROGRAM CONSULTANTS

Diana Lambdin
Frank Lester, Jr.
Kit Norris

CONTRIBUTING AUTHORS

Beth Lewis
Peter Stowasser
Allan Turton

ORIGO
EDUCATION

STUDENT JOURNAL

CONTENTS

MODULE 7

MODULE 8

MODULE 9

MODULE 10

MODULE 11

MODULE 12

FINANCIAL LITERACY

INTRODUCTION

The *ORIGO Stepping Stones* program has been created to provide a smarter way to teach and learn mathematics. It has been developed by a team of experts to provide a world-class math program.

STUDENT JOURNAL

Following are the features of the Grade K Student Journal as a part of the whole program.

PERFORATED PAGES

Young students need many hands-on experiences to sort, match, compare, and order quantities, pictures, words, and numerals long before they can write. The perforation in this journal allows students to remove and cut out images for use in activities such as these.

MODULE AND LESSON

Some lessons have more than one journal page.

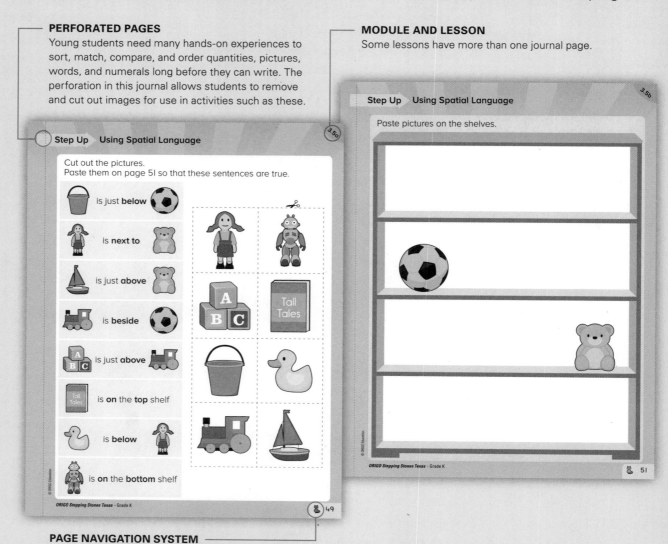

PAGE NAVIGATION SYSTEM

Most users of this book have not yet learned to read two-digit numbers. This journal provides a special navigation symbol at the bottom of each page. There is one unique symbol in a color sequence for each module. Rather than asking students to turn to a page number, the teacher can say, "Turn to the pink apple".

Financial Literacy

ORIGO's *Stepping Into Financial Literacy* is an online channel that addresses the Personal Financial Literacy standards of the *Texas Essential Knowledge and Skills* for Mathematics. For your convenience, the student pages from this resource are provided at the back of this journal (pages 181–191).

PRACTICE BOOK

Regular and meaningful practice is a hallmark of *ORIGO Stepping Stones*. Each module in the practice book has perforated pages that revisit content from an earlier module, and pages that practice numeral writing or computation.

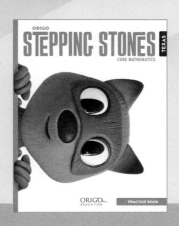

ORIGO Big Books build on young students' natural love for stories to help introduce key mathematical concepts. There are 12 Big Books at this grade.

The Number Case provides teachers with ready-made resources that are designed to develop students' understanding of number.

ADDITIONAL RESOURCES — ONLINE CHANNELS

These are some of the innovative teaching channels integrated into the teacher's online program.

ORIGO MathEd

Professional learning sessions

Flare

Interactive whiteboard tools

Fundamentals Game Boards

Interactive games

GLOSSARY

2D SHAPE

A **two-dimensional (2D) shape** shows length and width. A 2D shape can be made with only straight sides, only one curved side, or straight and curved sides. For example:

A triangle is a 2D shape with three straight sides.

A circle is a 2D shape made with one curve.

A square rectangle is a 2D shape with four straight sides that are all the same length. Sides across from each other are the same distance apart.

A non-square rectangle is a 2D shape with four straight sides. Pairs of sides across from each other are the same length and the same distance apart.

3D OBJECT

A **three-dimensional (3D) object** shows length, width, and height. A 3D object can be solid like a brick, hollow like a football, or skeletal like a house frame. For example:

A cone is a 3D object made with one flat surface and one curved surface.

A cylinder is a 3D object made with two flat surfaces and one curved surface.

A cube is a box-shaped 3D object made with six flat surfaces that are the same size.

A sphere is a ball-shaped 3D object made with one curved surface.

ADDITION

Addition is used to find the total or sum of two or more numbers of objects. This is recorded in an addition sentence that uses words or symbols. Addition is shown by the + symbol.

For example:

two bears **plus** three bears **is** five bears
or
$$2 \quad + \quad 3 \quad = \quad 5$$

EQUALS

When something **equals** something else it means "is the same as" or "balances". Equality is shown by the = symbol. For example, 2 add 3 balances 5 means 2 + 3 is the same as 5 or 2 + 3 = 5.

NUMBER

Number tells "how many". There are nine blocks in this group.

NUMBER FACTS

Addition facts are all the addition sentences that show two one-digit numbers being added. Addition facts can be written with the total or sum at the start or at the end.

For example: 2 + 3 = 5 or 3 = 1 + 2

Subtraction facts are all the subtraction sentences that are related to the addition facts.

For example: 5 − 2 = 3 or 3 − 2 = 1

NUMERAL

A **numeral** is the symbol used when recording a number.

PATTERNS

In **repeating** patterns, the repeating part stays the same.

For example:

In this pattern, the repeating part is .

In **growing or shrinking** patterns, each part "grows" or "shrinks" in some way that does not change.

For example:

In this pattern, each part grows by .

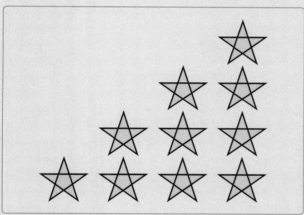

In this pattern, each part shrinks by .

SUBTRACTION

Subtraction involves taking one number away from another. Subtraction may be used to find an unknown addend or to find the difference between two numbers. This is recorded in a subtraction sentence that uses words or symbols. Subtraction is shown by the − symbol.

For example:

five bears **take away two** bears **is three** bears
or
5 − 2 = 3

TURNAROUND FACT

Each addition fact has a related **turnaround fact**.

For example:

2 + 3 = 5
3 + 2 = 5

YES/NO PICTURE GRAPH

A **yes/no picture graph** is a graphical record of responses to a question that only requires a "yes" or "no" answer.

For example:

Do you own a pet?	
	😊
	😊
	😊
😊	😊
😊	😊
😊	😊
😊	😊
😊	😊
yes	no

Step Up

Creating Sets of Pictures to Match Numerals and Number Names

Color balls to match.

four 4	
two 2	    
one 1	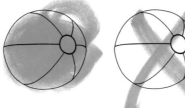   
five 5	
three 3	    

Step Up   Sorting into Two Categories

Cut out these pictures. Then sort and paste them on page 17.

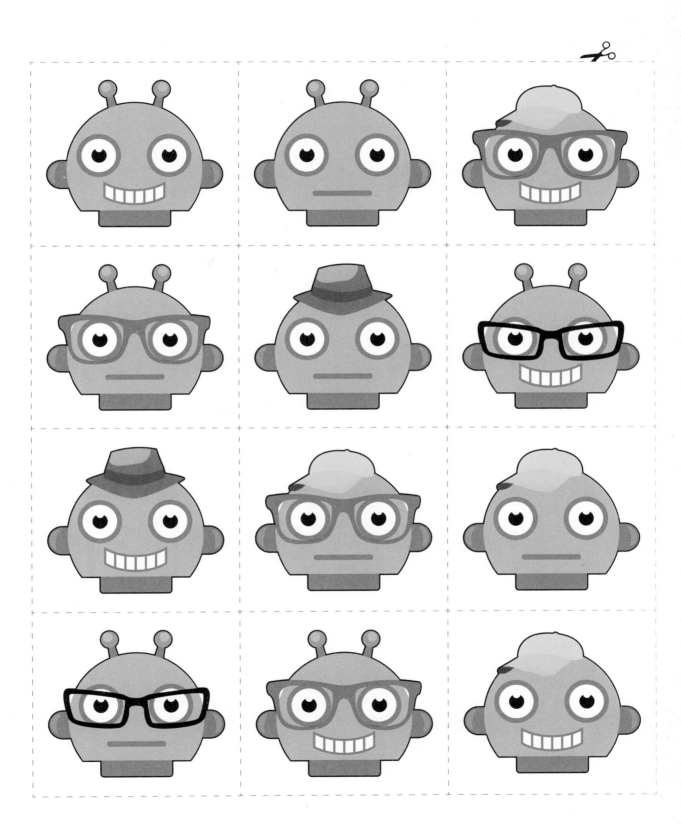

15

Name

Paste the pictures in the boxes below to show your sorting.

Name

Step Up   Matching Quantities

Paste the dominoes on the trail. Match the number of dots.

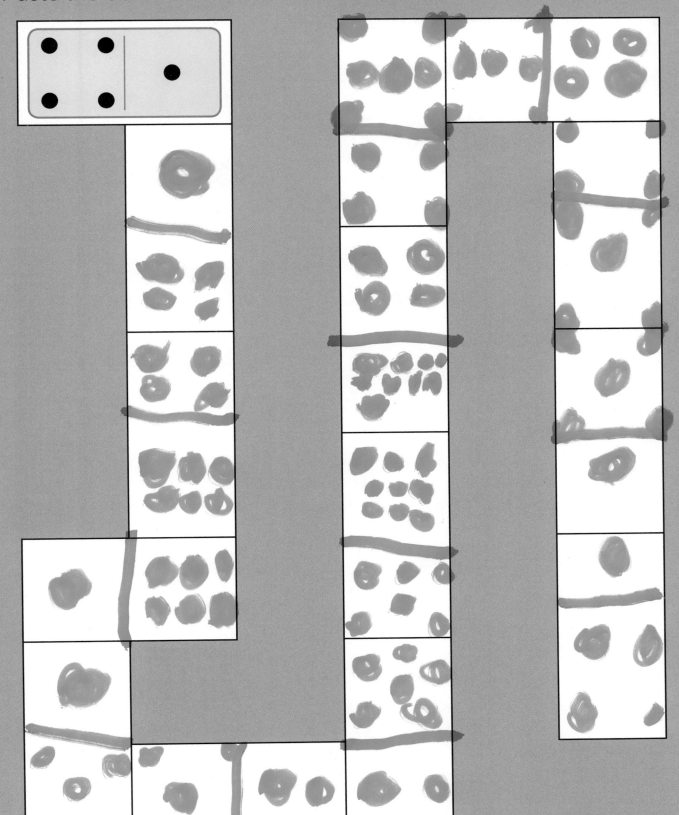

Step Up Writing Numerals 1 to 6

Follow the arrows. Trace then write the matching numerals.

one

four

six

Step Up Making Yes/No Picture Graphs

Cut out the faces. Then use them with the graph on page 39.

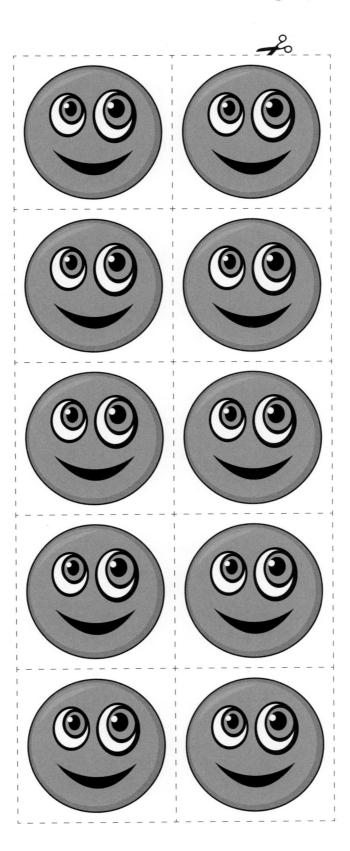

Step Up ▶ Making Yes/No Picture Graphs

Paste faces in the graph to show yes or no.

Have you been on an airplane?

yes	no

Name

Step Up — Writing Numerals Just Before and Just After (1 to 9)

Write the numerals that come **just after** and **just before**.

| 1 | 2 | 3 | 4 | 5 | 6 | 7 | 8 | 9 |

just after

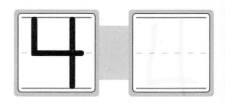

just before

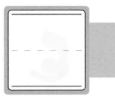

Name

Step Up Using Spatial Language

Paste pictures on the shelves.

Cut out the numeral cards to use on page 61.

1	2
3	4
5	6
7	8
9	10

Step Up   Comparing 1 to 10 Represented as Numerals

Paste cards in the boxes. Loop the **greater** number in each pair.

	Card		Card
	Card		Card
	Card		Card
	Card		Card
	Card		Card

Step Up Comparing Length

Color blue the pictures that are **shorter** than your string.
Color yellow the pictures that are **longer** than your string.

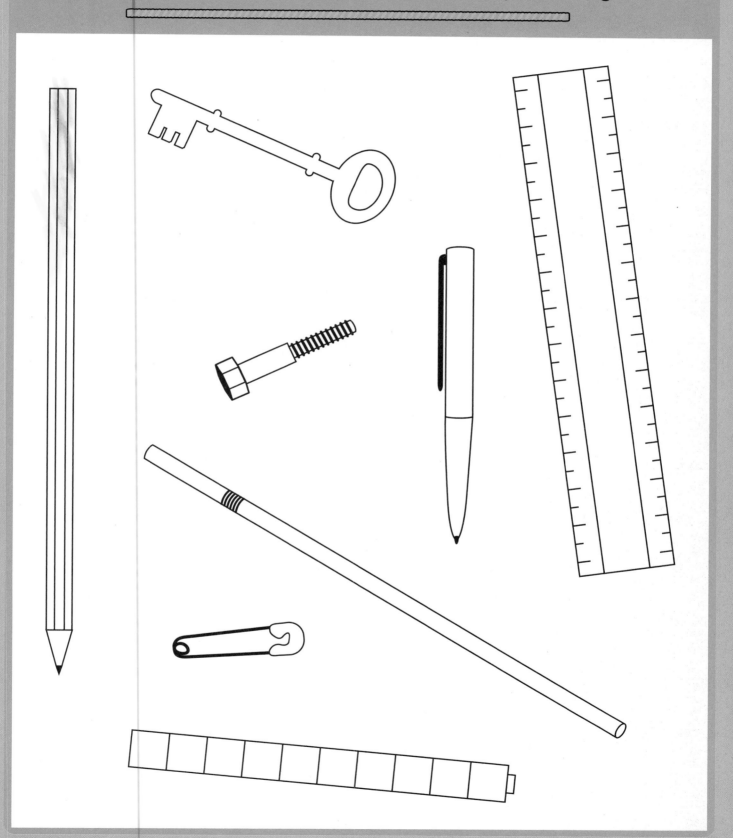

Name

Step Up Comparing and Ordering Length

Cut out the pictures.
Then paste each above a matching label on page 67.

Name

Step Up   Comparing and Ordering Length

Paste the hats, pants, and ties above the matching label.

	taller	tallest
	wider	widest
	shorter	shortest

Step Up ▸ Representing 0 to 10

Cut out these cards.
Paste them on the matching pictures on page 75.

✂

7	10	1
0	8	3
6	5	9
2	4	
four	ten	six
three	eight	zero
five	seven	one
two	nine	

Step Up ▸ Representing 0 to 10

Paste the numeral and number name on the matching quantity.

Step Up ▶ Continuing Growing Patterns

Draw the next picture in each pattern.

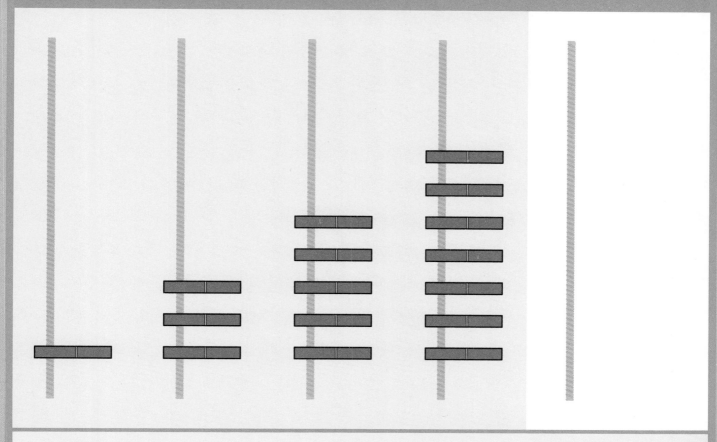

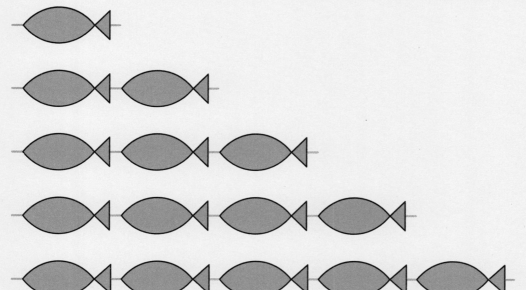

Step Up ▷ Introducing the Addition Concept (Active Stories)

Write the number in each group. Then write how many in total.

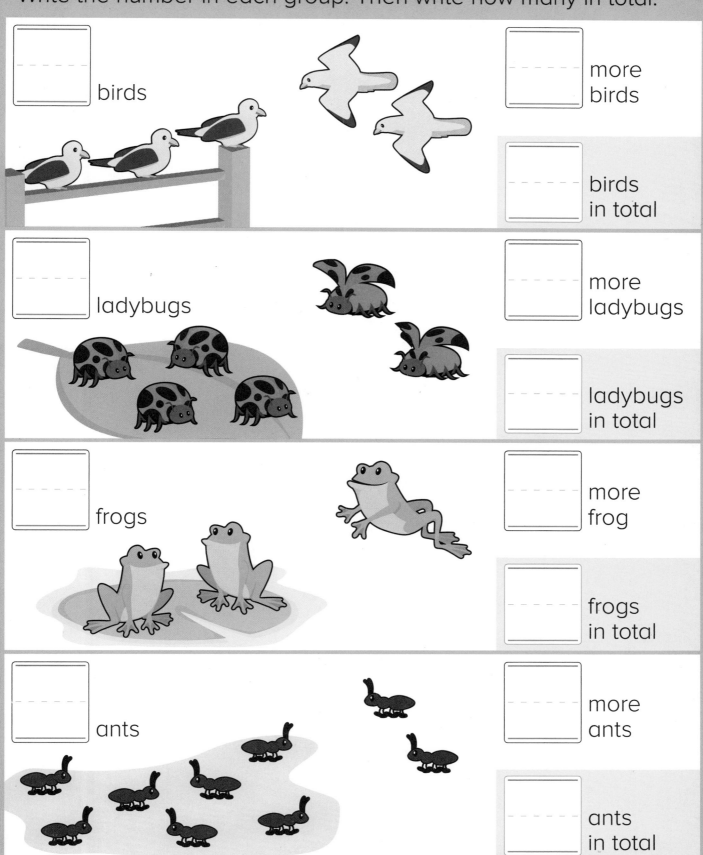

birds

more birds

birds in total

ladybugs

more ladybugs

ladybugs in total

frogs

more frog

frogs in total

ants

more ants

ants in total

Step Up ▸ Adding Two Groups

Use two colors to show two groups.
Then write the number in each part and the total.

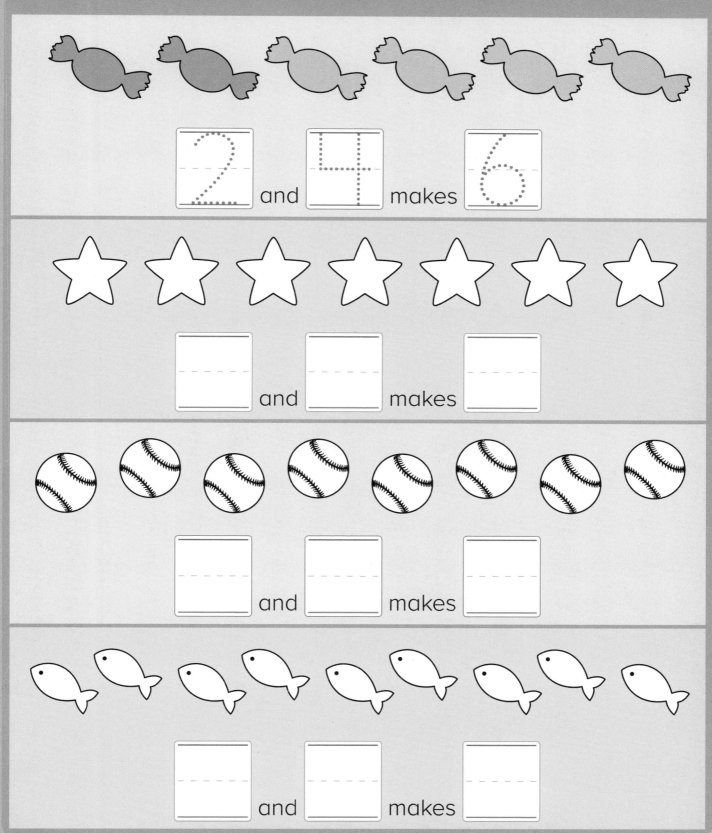

2 and 4 makes 6

and ___ makes ___

and ___ makes ___

and ___ makes ___

Name

Step Up ▶ Writing Addition Sentences

Draw more faces to fill the frame.
Then complete the addition sentence.

a.

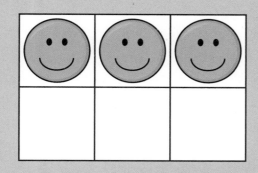

3 add ☐ makes ☐

b.

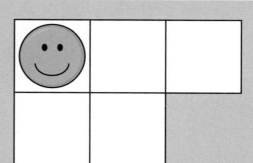

 add makes

c.

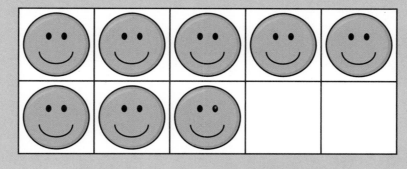

 add  makes ☐

d.

 add makes ☐

Step Up ▶ Working with Addition

Write the amount in the purse.
Write the amount being added. Then write the total.

a.

$\boxed{}$ add $\boxed{}$ is $\boxed{}$ pennies.

b.

$\boxed{}$ add $\boxed{}$ is $\boxed{}$ pennies.

c.

$\boxed{}$ add $\boxed{}$ is $\boxed{}$ pennies.

d.

$\boxed{}$ add $\boxed{}$ is $\boxed{}$ pennies.

e.

$\boxed{}$ add $\boxed{}$ is $\boxed{}$ pennies.

Step Up · Comparing Weight

Draw some things that you know are **heavier** than a .

Draw some things that you know are **lighter** than a full .

Step Up Introducing the Pan Balance

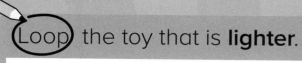 the toy that is **lighter**.

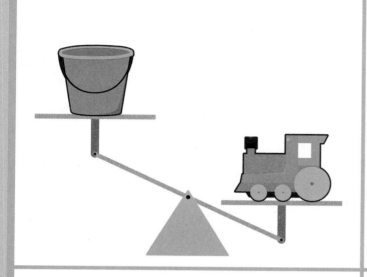

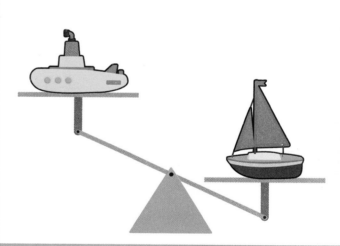

Draw a matching number of shapes.
Then trace over the number name.

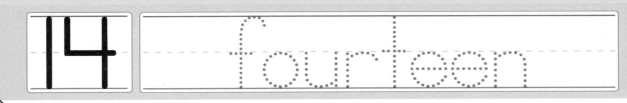

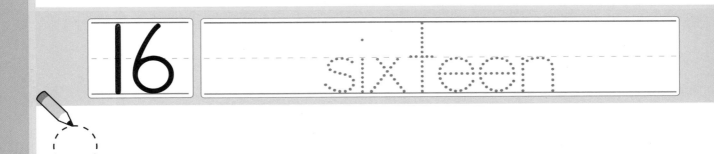

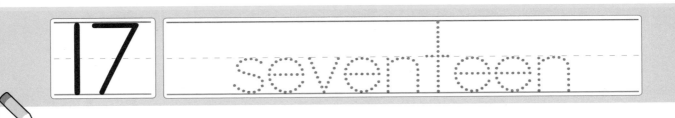

Name

Step Up ▶ Matching Representations for 19, 18, and 15

Stamp the matching number of shapes.
Then trace over the number name.

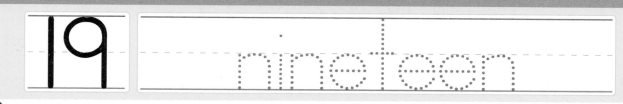

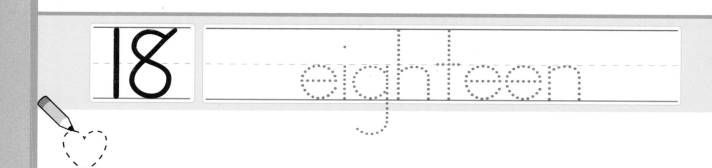

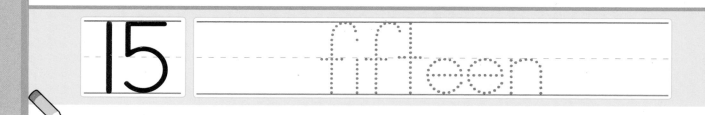

Name

Step Up   Matching Representations for 13, 12, and 11

Stamp the matching number of shapes.
Then trace over the number name.

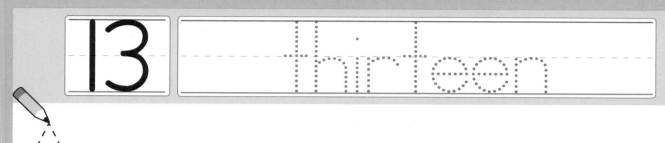

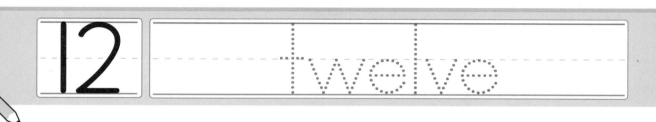

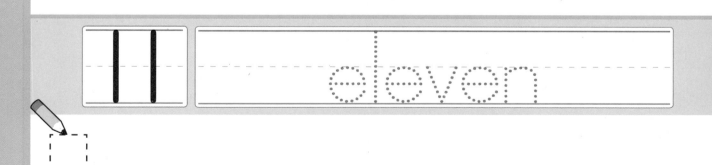

Step Up ▶ **Representing 11 to 20**

Cut out these cards.
Then paste them on the matching pictures on page 105.

✂

17	20	11
14	18	13
16	15	19
12		

fourteen	twenty	sixteen
thirteen	eighteen	nineteen
fifteen	twelve	eleven
seventeen		

Step Up Representing 11 to 20

Paste the numeral and number name on the matching quantity.

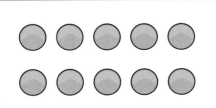
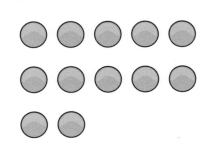
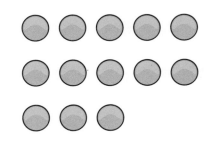

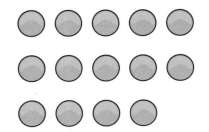
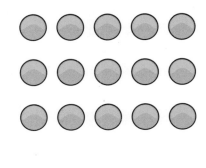
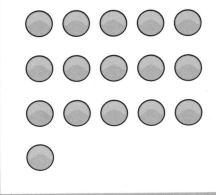

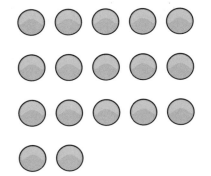
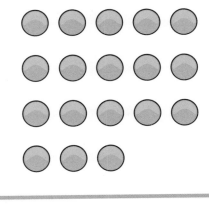
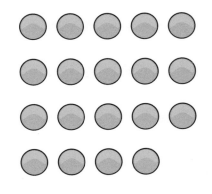

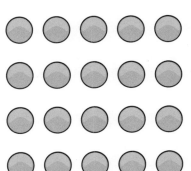

Step Up ▶ Sorting 3D Objects

Cut out the pictures.
Then sort and paste them where they belong on page 109.

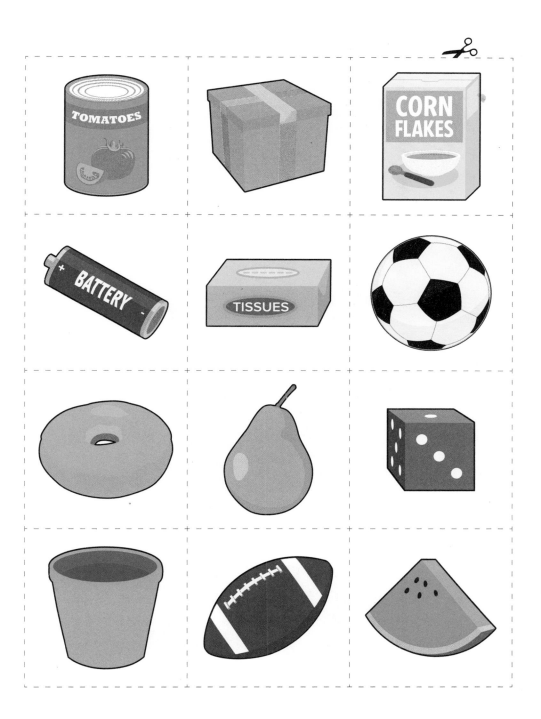

Name

Step Up ▶ Sorting 3D Objects

Sort and paste the pictures where they belong.

all flat surfaces

all curved surfaces

both flat and curved surfaces

Step Up ▸ Identifying 3D Objects

Cut out the names and the pictures.
Paste them where they belong on page 113.

✂

| sphere | cube | cone | cylinder |

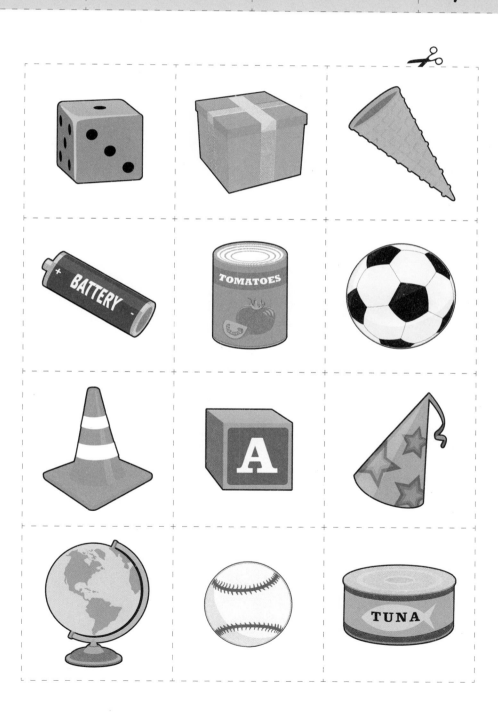

Name

Step Up ▶ Identifying 3D Objects

Paste the matching name below each object.
Then sort and paste the pictures where they belong.

Name

Step Up   Introducing the Idea of Balance

Draw ⬤ in each empty box to make each balance picture true.
Then write the addition sentence to match.

a.

_____ and _____ balances _____

b.

_____ and _____ balances _____

c.

_____ and _____ balances _____

d.

_____ balances _____ and _____

Name

Step Up Identifying an Unknown Part in Balance Situations

Draw ◯ in each empty box to make each balance picture true.
Then write the addition sentence to match.

a.

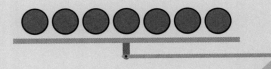

_____ add _____ is the same as _____

b.

_____ is the same as _____ add _____

c.

_____ add _____ is the same as _____

d.

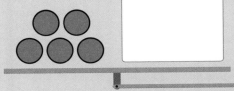

_____ is the same as _____ add _____

Step Up ▶ Identifying Two Parts that Balance a Total

Draw ◯ in each empty box to make each balance picture true. Then write the addition sentence to match.

a.

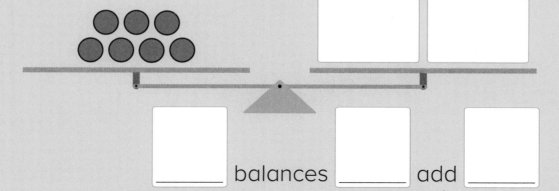

_____ balances _____ add _____

b.

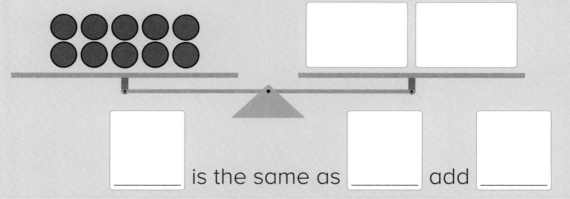

_____ is the same as _____ add _____

c.

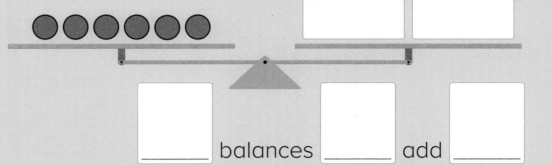

_____ balances _____ add _____

d.

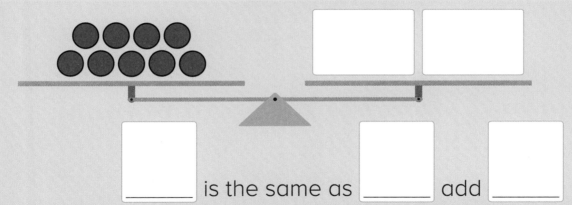

_____ is the same as _____ add _____

Step Up ▶ Developing the Language of Equality

Draw ⬤ in each empty box to make each balance picture true.
Then write the addition sentence to match.

a.

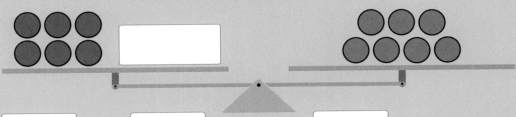

_____ add _____ balances _____

b.

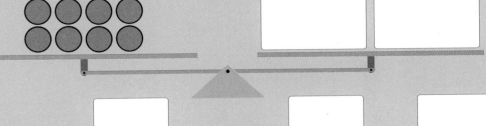

_____ is equal to _____ add _____

c.

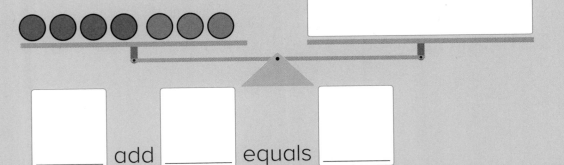

_____ add _____ equals _____

d.

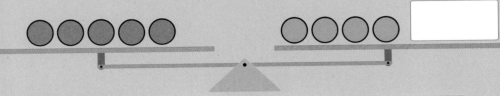

_____ = _____ add _____

Name

Step Up Identifying and Using 3D Objects

Loop the **cones** in yellow.
Loop the **cylinders** in blue.
Loop the **cubes** in green.
Loop the **spheres** in red.

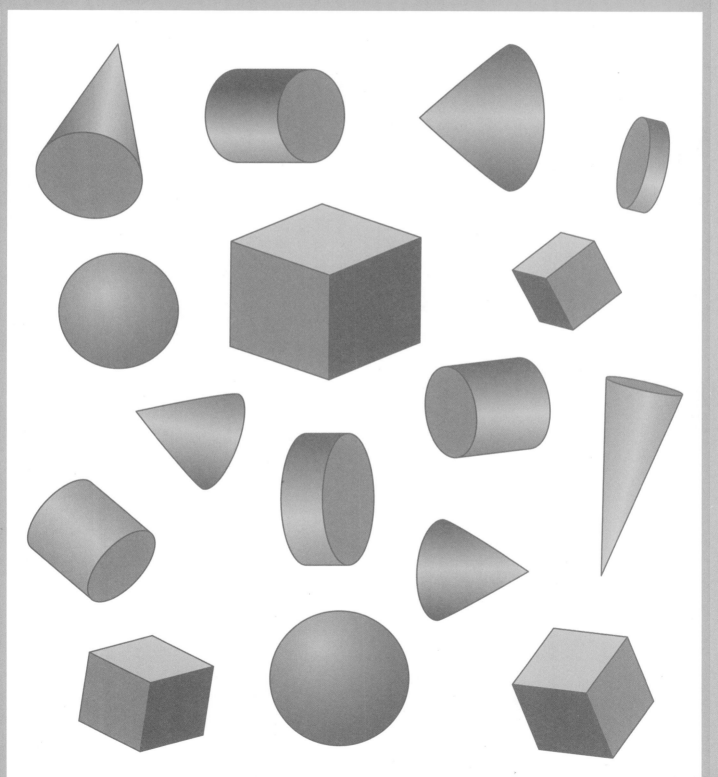

Step Up Sorting 2D Shapes and 3D Objects

Cut out the pictures.
Then sort and paste them where they belong on page 127.

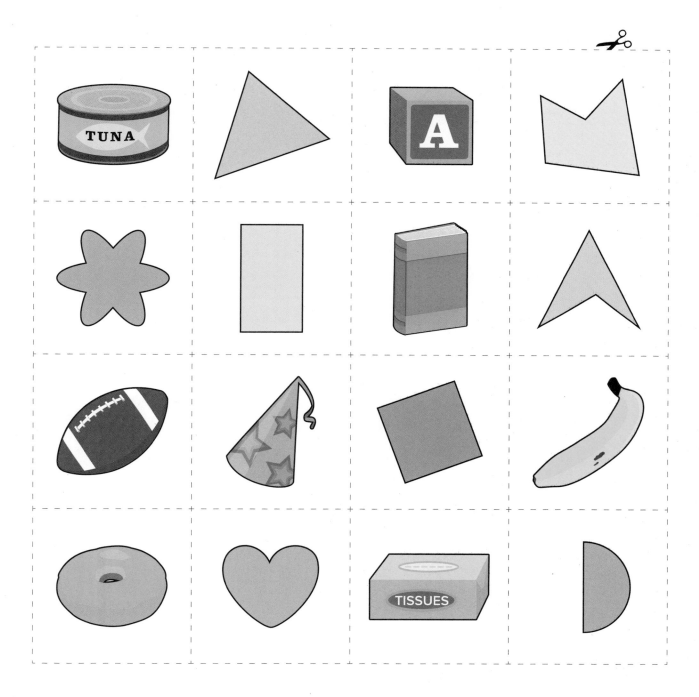

Name

Sort the 2D shapes and pictures of 3D objects.
Paste them where they belong.

2D shapes

pictures of 3D objects

Step Up ▸ Writing Addition Sentences (with Symbols)

Color the mice. Then write a matching addition sentence.

a.   Color 3 mice brown.

⬜ + ⬜ = ⬜

b.   Color 5 mice brown.

⬜ + ⬜ = ⬜

c.   Color 2 mice brown.

⬜ + ⬜ = ⬜

d.   Color 4 mice brown.

⬜ + ⬜ = ⬜

Name

Step Up ▸ Using the Commutative Property of Addition

Write two addition sentences to match each domino.

a. 2 + 5 = ☐

☐ dots

5 + 2 = ☐

b. ☐ + ☐ = ☐

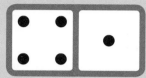

☐ + ☐ = ☐

c. ☐ + ☐ = ☐

☐ + ☐ = ☐

d. ☐ + ☐ = ☐

☐ + ☐ = ☐

e. ☐ + ☐ = ☐

☐ + ☐ = ☐

f. ☐ + ☐ = ☐

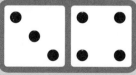

☐ + ☐ = ☐

Step Up ▸ Introducing the "Think Big, Count Small" Idea

Complete the addition sentence. Write the **greater** number first.

a.

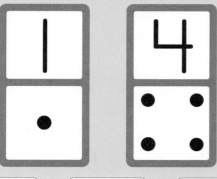

⬜ + ⬜ = ⬜

b.

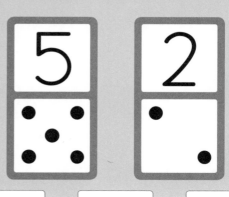

⬜ + ⬜ = ⬜

c.

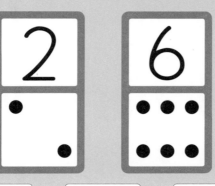

⬜ + ⬜ = ⬜

d.

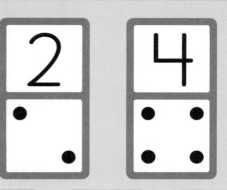

⬜ + ⬜ = ⬜

e.

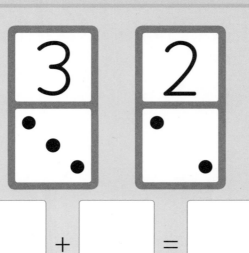

⬜ + ⬜ = ⬜

f.

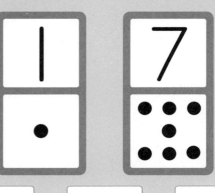

⬜ + ⬜ = ⬜

Step Up Identifying Two Parts that Total 10

Draw more dots to make 10. Then complete the addition sentence.

a.

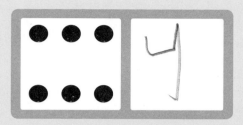

$6 + 4 = 10$

b.

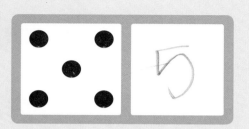

$10 = 5 + 5$

c.

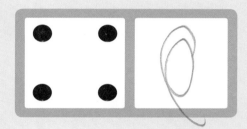

$4 + 6 = 10$

d.

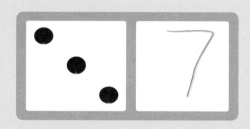

$10 = 3 + 7$

e.

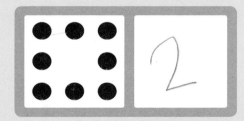

$8 + 2 = 10$

f.

$10 = 7 + 3$

Step Up ▶ Analyzing Attributes of 2D Shapes

Write the number of sides and corners for each shape.

a.

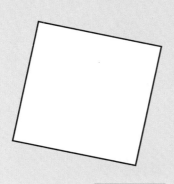

 sides   corners

b.

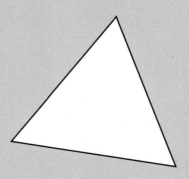

_____ sides   _____ corners

c.

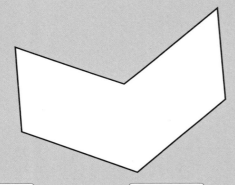

 sides   corners

d.

_____ sides   corners

e.

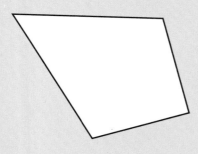

 sides   corners

f.

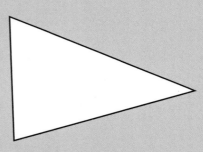

 sides   corners

Step Up Identifying 2D Shapes

Cut out the 2D shapes.
Then sort and paste them where they belong on page 141.

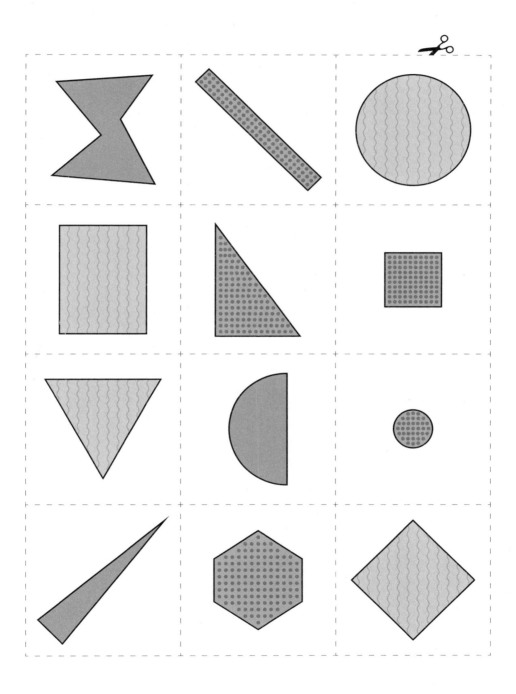

Step Up Identifying 2D Shapes

Sort the 2D shapes and paste them where they belong.

triangles

circles

square rectangles

non-square rectangles

other shapes

Step Up > Analyzing Teen Numbers

Loop 10 shapes. Count how many more and write the number to match.

a.

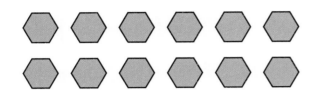

ten and [ ] more

b.

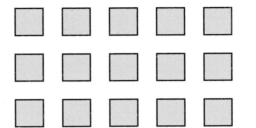

ten and [ ] more

c.

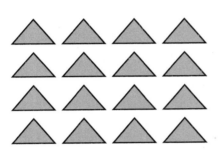

ten and [ ] more

d.

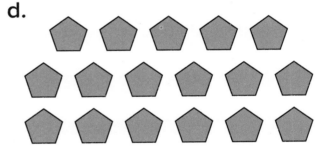

ten and [ ] more

e.

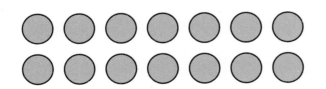

ten and [ ] more

f.

ten and [ ] more

Step Up ▶ Working with Teen Numbers

Write the number of tens and ones.

a.

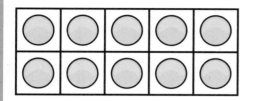

_____ ten and _____ ones

b.

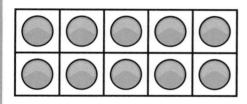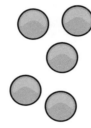

_____ ten and _____ ones

c.

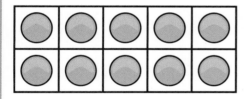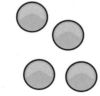

_____ ten and _____ ones

d.

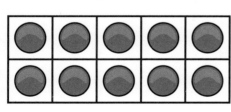

_____ ten and _____ ones

e.

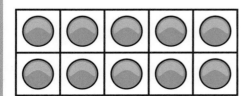

_____ ten and _____ ones

Step Up

Generating Quantities that are One More or One Less (1 to 20)

Write the number of counters in each picture. Draw counters to show **one more**. Then draw counters to show **one less**.

one less		one more

Step Up

Writing Numbers that are One More and One Less (1 to 20)

149

Write the numbers that are **one less** and **one more**.

| 1 | 2 | 3 | 4 | 5 | 6 | 7 | 8 | 9 | 10 | 11 | 12 | 13 | 14 | 15 | 16 | 17 | 18 | 19 | 20 |

a.

one less   one more

b.

one less   one more

c.

one less   one more

d.

one less   one more

e.

one less   one more

f.

one less   one more

g.

one less   one more

h.

one less   one more

Step Up Drawing 2D Shapes

Copy each picture.

Cut out the 12 shapes and paste them on page 155.

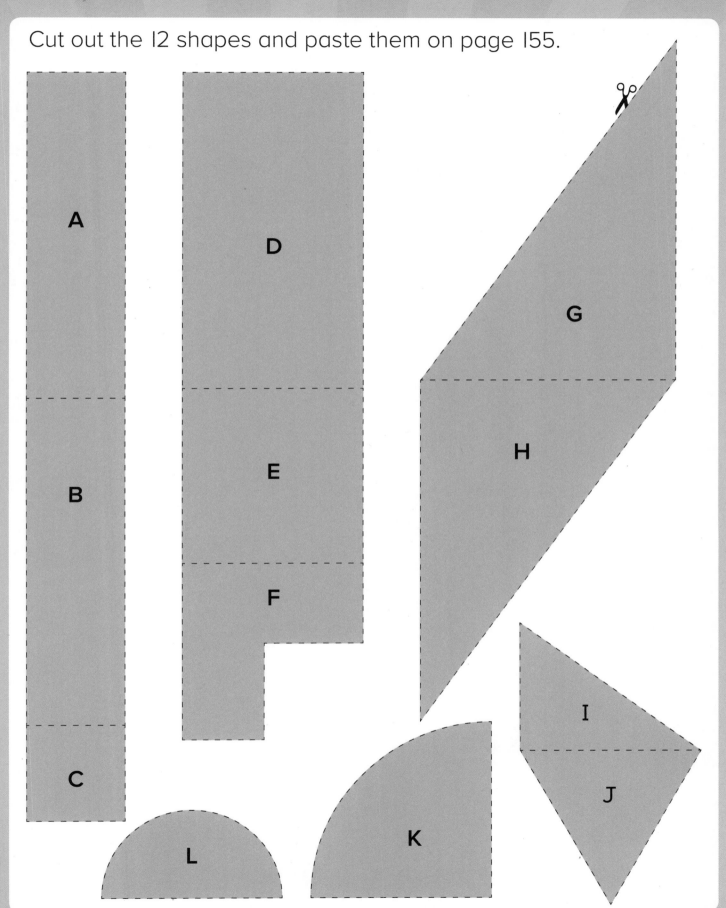

Step Up ▶ Creating 2D Shapes

Paste two shapes to match each outline.

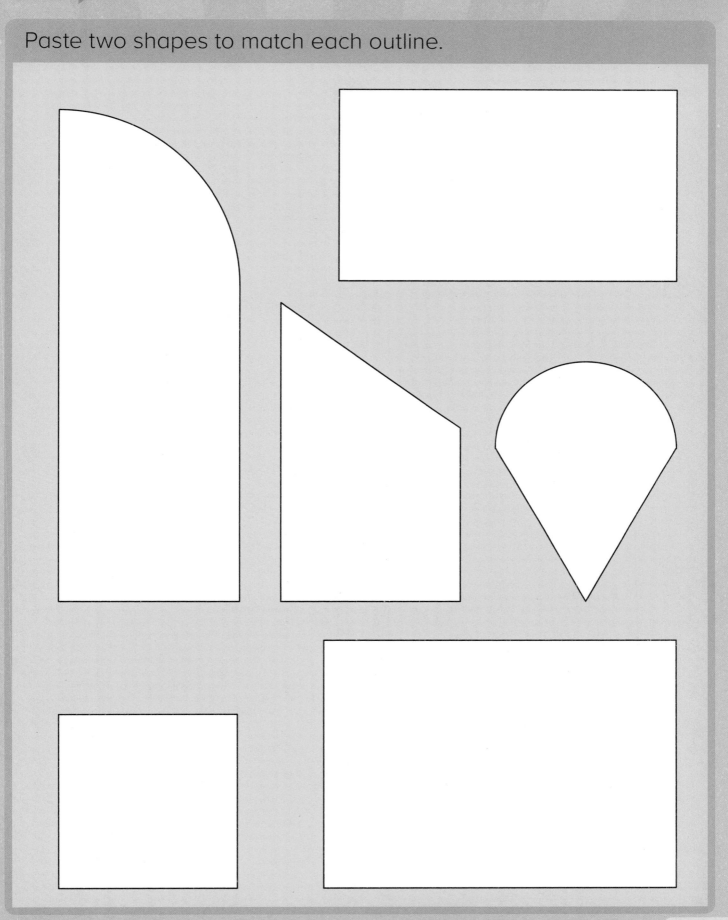

Write numbers to match each picture.

a.

_____ birds in total

_____ fly away

b.

_____ ladybugs in total

_____ fly away

c.

_____ frogs in total

_____ jumps away

d.

_____ chickens in total

_____ walk away

e.

_____ bees in total

_____ buzz away

f.

_____ ants in total

_____ walk away

Step Up ▸ Representing Subtraction Situations

Draw more objects to show the total.
Then read the sentence and **cross out** the number shown.

8 balls One rolls away.	
6 books Four fall down.	
7 eggs Three break.	
9 balloons Two go pop.	
5 crayons Two are lost.	
8 badges Take away four.	

Name

Step Up › Writing Subtraction Sentences

Write the total. Cover 1 or 2 dots. Then write the number that are left.

a.

5 cover 2 = ☐

b.

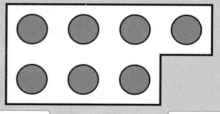

☐ cover 1 = ☐

c.

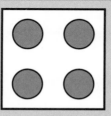

☐ cover 1 = ☐

d.

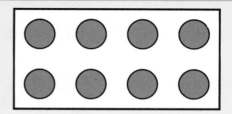

☐ cover 2 = ☐

e.

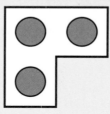

☐ cover 2 = ☐

f.

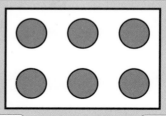

☐ cover 1 = ☐

g.

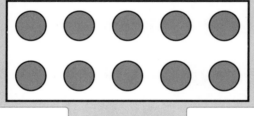

☐ cover 1 = ☐

h.

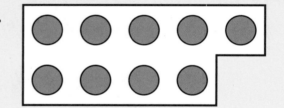

☐ cover 2 = ☐

Name

Step Up Writing Subtraction Sentences (with Symbols)

Write the subtraction sentence to match the picture.

a.

| 4 | − | 1 | = | |

b.

| | − | | = | |

c.

| | − | | = | |

d.

| | − | | = | |

e.

| | − | | = | |

f.

| | − | | = | |

Step Up ▸ Identifying Coins

1. Draw a line to match each coin to its name.

2. Think about the size of each coin. Then draw a line to match each coin outline to the coin name. Use real coins to help.

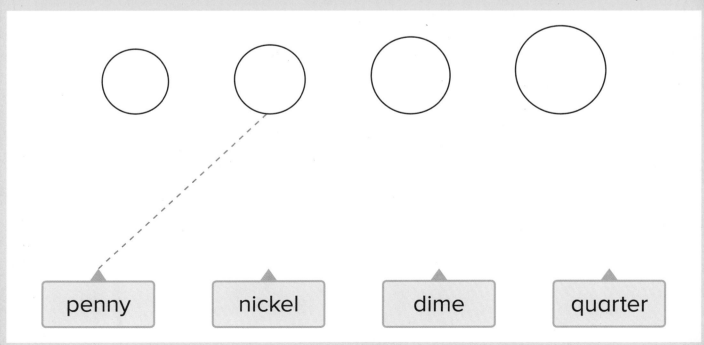

Step Up ▶ Working with Pennies

I. Color pennies to match.

a. Color 10 cents.

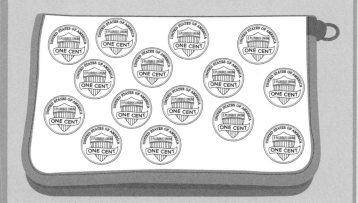

b. Color 13 cents.

c. Color 15 cents.

d. Color 11 cents.

2. Trace around more pennies to show 7 cents in total.

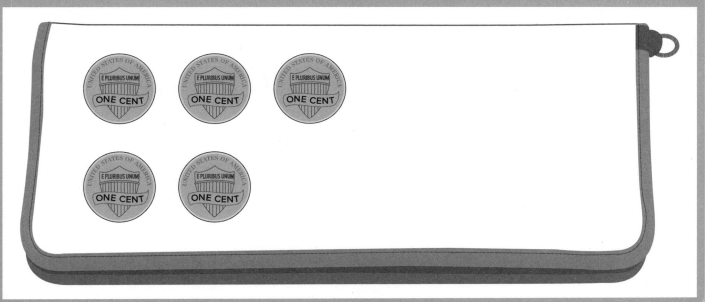

Step Up > Interpreting Addition and Subtraction Word Problems

Loop **+** or **−** to show how to solve each problem.

a.
Ashley has 8 dollars.
She spends 2 dollars at the store.
How much money does she have left?

+ **−**

b.
9 friends are in a swimming pool.
2 friends get out.
How many friends are still in the pool?

+ **−**

c.
4 dogs have short hair.
5 dogs have long hair.
How many dogs are there in total?

+ **−**

d.
There are 7 pennies in the purse.
2 more pennies are dropped into the purse.
How many pennies are in the purse now?

+ **−**

e.
David buys 6 baseball cards.
He gives 2 cards to Jude.
How many cards does David have now?

+ **−**

f.
8 horses are in the stable.
2 horses are in the field.
How many horses are there in total?

+ **−**

g.
There are 5 muffins on the tray.
2 muffins are banana. The rest are berry.
How many muffins are berry?

+ **−**

Name

Use blocks to act out each problem. Then write a number sentence to show the answer.

a. 7 birds were sitting on the fence. One bird flew away. How many birds are left?

b. Diana counts 3 blue cars and 3 red cars. How many cars did she count in total?

c. There are 10 players in the soccer team. 3 players are boys. The rest are girls. How many girls are in the team?

d. Awan packs 2 toys in the box. Nicole packs 6 more toys in the same box. How many toys are now in the box?

e. Hugo has 6 strawberries and 4 blueberries. How many berries does Hugo have in total?

f. 3 friends are playing on the swings. 6 more friends join them. How many friends are now playing?

Step Up

Solving Addition and Subtraction Word Problems (Drawing Pictures)

Draw pictures to solve each problem. Then write a number sentence to show the answer.

a. There are 5 balls. 2 balls roll away. How many balls are left?

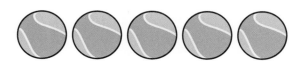

b. 4 crayons are red. 2 crayons are green. How many crayons are there in total?

c. There are 6 eggs. One egg is broken. How many eggs are left?

d. Akeema has 3 pennies. She finds 4 more pennies. How many pennies does she have now?

Step Up

Solving Addition and Subtraction Word Problems (Number Sentences)

Write a number sentence to solve each problem.

a. 5 friends are playing in the pool. 2 friends get out of the water. How many friends are left in the pool?

b. Fatima scored 2 goals in the first game. She scored 4 goals in the next game. How many goals did she score in total?

c. Toby has 9 baseball cards. He loses 3 cards. How many baseball cards does he now have?

d. The zoo has 4 adult tigers and 3 tiger cubs. How many tigers are there at the zoo?

e. There are 6 fish in the tank. 2 fish are hiding. How many fish can be seen?

f. There are 3 horses and 4 cows on a farm. How many animals are there in total?

Name

Step Up > Discussing Short and Long Time Durations

Write **S** for each activity that takes a **short** time.
Write **L** for each activity that takes a **long** time.

Step Up ▸ Ordering the Days of the Week

a. Draw lines to connect the days **in order**.
Start and **finish** on Sunday.

● Wednesday

Monday ●   ● Friday

Saturday ●   ● Sunday

Thursday ●   ● Tuesday

b. Write the day that is **just before** Tuesday.

c. Write the day that is **just after** Friday.

d. How many days in one week?

Name

STEPPING INTO
FINANCIAL LITERACY

CONTENTS

Financial Literacy

Identifying Ways to Earn Income

Cut out the pictures.
Then sort and paste them where they belong on page 185.

Identifying Ways to Earn Income

Sort and paste the pictures where they belong.

earning an income	not earning an income

Name

Distinguishing between Money Earned and Money Received as a Gift

Draw a picture of a person earning money.

money earned

Draw a picture of a person receiving money as a gift.

money received as a gift

Identifying Simple Skills for Jobs

Financial Literacy

Write skills to match each job.

doctor

waiter

Distinguishing between Wants and Needs

Loop **want** or **need**.

want	need

want	need

want	need

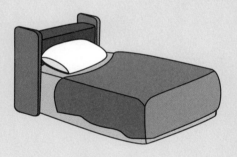

want	need

Draw pictures to match.

I want	I need

Coins

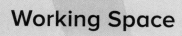

Working Space